CW00567000

COMPOS

MAYE E. BRUCE

Practical Advice on Nature's Method of Restoring Life in the Soil.

FIRST PUBLISHED 1947
SECOND EDITION 1948
THIRD REVISED EDITION 1953
FOURTH REVISED EDITION 2009 - EDITED BY ANDREW E. DAVENPORT

Text © Maye E. Bruce

Published by
QR Composting Solutions, Newcastle upon Tyne, UK
www.qrcompostingsolutions.co.uk

Design and layout: Ian Scott Design

Printed and bound in Great Britain by Cambridge Scholars Publishing

Printed on recycled paper containing 100% post consumer waste

British Library Cataloguing in Publication Data.
A catalogue record of this book is available from the British Library.

ISBN 978-0-9560087-1-8

Editor's Preface

This booklet has been reprinted with the kind permission of Chase Organics who originally published and printed this practical and useful guide to Quick Return compost making. Where the original booklet contains weights and measures in imperial units, in this revised edition the metric and modern equivalents have been given. Certain statements in the original booklet have relevance to the particular era and these have been left as they are for integrity. For similar reasons where prices are quoted they have been left unchanged.

As I believe Miss Bruce may have wished, the main aim in reproducing this booklet is to pass on the legacy of QR compost making and in doing so 'Give back life to the soil eventually abolishing disease in plant, animal and man'.

In today's terms there is a job to do in saving our endangered planet from the perils of climate change and to relieve our dependence on fossil fuels. In my humble opinion this all starts with sustainability at home and in the garden where we can make a difference by QR composting our waste, feeding the soil and growing our own food. In short, the time has returned where we must 'Dig for Victory' once again.

I would like to express my sincere thanks to Lady Illife of Berkshire for her inspired idea of reprinting this booklet.

Andrew E Davenport

Chapter 1

WHY COMPOST ?

"Where there is no life in the soil the plants perish." That is a paraphrase - it is also the subject of this book. "Life in the Soil" — How does it start? Here are two pictures:

First picture. The lower slopes of a volcano — no plants — no life — the ground still hot enough to be uncomfortable. A little lower down the slope it is cooler — still no plants, but there *is* a tiny patch of bright yellow lichen, the lowest form of plant life and *that* is the start of life in the soil. The lichen dies, is disintegrated by bacteria and makes a minute covering of humus — of living soil. Other lowly plants, larger lichens and mosses follow, die and equally become humus. By degrees the face of the lava rocks crumbles slowly under the weather; it amalgamates with the humus and the soil deepens, till eventually it is deep enough to receive and feed a chance seed dropped by a bird or blown by the wind, and so the process continues. The dead soil begins to live.

Second picture. A tropical forest - hot, humid - with intense pressure of vegetable growth and decay; plants die, and bacteria convert them into humus almost as they reach the soil — it is an orgy of plant life, terrifying in its power.

Between these two extremes is the temperate, fertile soil of England, now faced with a serious dilemma. In the old days when farmyard manure was plentiful and sold at 2s. 6d. a load, the feeding of farm and garden was simple. Today, farmyard manure costs ten or twenty times as much and is often practically unobtainable except for the farmers themselves, and even they have not enough to meet their needs. Over-cropping by the use of artificial stimulants in the soil, reckless felling of trees and other shortsighted 'cash return' methods have destroyed much of the essential life in the soil, and there is growing demand for the return to a natural way of rebuilding and maintaining the fertility of our land.

How can we restore life to tired soil, supply our growing crops with the food which they need and keep them healthy and free from disease? By making compost and applying it to the soil, and so encouraging the soil organisms to do most of our work for us. We are only just beginning to realise the super-importance of this unseen labour force in making and keeping the soil fertile and in maintaining health, growth and vigour in our growing crops. Compost will not only supply them with many of their needs but will stimulate the multiplication of the micro-flora, bacteria and fungi; and of the beneficial large and small soil fauna, all of which depend for their existence on a liberal supply of semi-decayed organic matter.

Let us take the micro-flora group first. Their weight in one acre of fertile top-soil is estimated at 40 tons (40 tonnes). There are many different kinds, each with their own work, and the activities of the various species are gradually becoming known. Some draw nitrogen from the air; some act as 'police'; if one species grows too numerous another develops and attacks, and so the balance is maintained. Some free the locked-up minerals, which include phosphates and trace elements, so essential to plant health, and convert them into food for plants. In the great majority of the soils of the world, though there are some exceptions, all minerals are present, but in a humus-deficient soil they are locked up and out of reach of the plant roots. It is for this reason that soil chemists have hitherto been convinced that the addition of 'artificials' was essential to supply the necessary minerals the plant needs. We now know that the action of certain species of this vast army of bacteria, which find ideal conditions for reproduction in a well-made compost heap, will do the job just as thoroughly and in a far safer way.

Next, there are enormous numbers of minute soil fauna, the Springtails, the Mites and the Centipedes and many others sufficiently large to be seen with the naked eye. It has been found that the number of these creatures varies greatly with the quality of the soil: in good garden soil the count is far higher than in poor pasture land; in compost the number is higher still. Sufficient is now known about the habits of the various groups of eelworm to indicate that if eelworm infested soil is treated with adequate supplies of well-made compost it will regain its normal balance.

Lastly, there are the earthworms, whose value to the soil was realised by Darwin over a hundred years ago. They are only to be found in a fertile soil, rich in humus. It is the earthworms which are responsible for the texture of the soil, for they create the vertical shafts which allow air to reach the roots of growing plants. They also release mineral foods from the soil which would otherwise be unavailable to the plants, for their digestive juices dissolve nutrients which are not water-soluble and so make them available. This is why worm-casts are up to twenty times as rich in available plant nutrients as the surrounding soil.

Chapter 2.
BUILDING THE HEAP

Turn the waste produce of your own garden and land into humus by composting it.

Some people complain — "Compost? Not for me! It smells so foul." "It needs so much labour." "It takes so long to ripen."

Nonsense!! If you build a heap correctly, there is no smell. If you build it systematically, there is little more labour than is involved in handling your waste material, and you have to handle it, even to burn it. The work will soon fit in with the routine on farm, holding or garden — and NO TURNING is required. Finally, if you use the Quick Return Herbal Activator (Q.R. for short) your heaps will turn to rich, ripe compost in from 4 to 8 weeks, according to the time of year - a compost that will bring back and increase the life in your soil and will do so by following nature's basic law, *i.e.*, the endless cycle of the return of life back to life.

If you realise what happens in a compost heap you cannot fail in making one. The compost heap is really a workshop! A great community of micro-organisms —bacteria of all kinds, maggots, insects and earthworms; all groups work on their own special jobs in the task of breaking down vegetable matter. The organisms are alive, they must breathe — therefore they need air; it is their respiration that creates the natural heat found in every well-built heap. This heat hastens decomposition, but it is easily lost, therefore the heap needs protection. Heavy rain or bad drainage will exclude air by saturation, therefore the heap needs shelter. The golden rule is: **Keep the heat in, the rain out and let the heap breathe.**

Any heap that is well built will eventually go to soil, but it will take a year or more to do so. By using Q.R. you will cut down the time to from 4 to 8 weeks, according to the time of the year, and will increase the richness of the compost itself.

BIN. Now for the details of building.

The ideal way is to make the heap in a bin — a box without a bottom. Suit the size to your garden, roughly from 2 ft. (60cm) square for a small plot to 6 ft. (180cm) for a larger one. Ventilate the bin by air holes in the sides or by narrow gaps between the boards.

FOUNDATION. If the soil is heavy and holding, make a rubble foundation for drainage. If it is light, build directly on the soil, with a layer of twigs or woody stems at the bottom. Do not build on concrete, which effectively stops all drainage and prevents the migration of worms and other soil organisms to the heap.

MATERIAL. Use all and any vegetable waste that is soft enough to cut with a spade and use it as fresh as possible; use weeds, spent annuals, hedge clippings, bracken, lawn mowings, autumn clearings, tea leaves and coffee grounds, vegetable trimmings from the kitchen, egg shells, dust from the vacuum cleaner, etc. It is wiser to omit remnants of fat, cheese rinds, etc. as these are liable to attract rats. Such wastes are better used for a neighbour's chickens (or your own) or the pig bin.

Animal manure is excellent if available. Poultry manure should be used in proportions 5% to 10%; stable, farmyard, rabbit and goat manure up to 20%. If the animal ingredient is not to hand, a perfectly satisfactory compost can be produced by using vegetable wastes only, providing it is treated with Q.R. to activate it. (see page 10)

BUILDING. Mix the different textures together, i.e., the soft green with the more fibrous stems and drier stuff. Do this by either building in alternate layers, or better still, chop all materials with a sharp spade to 4-inch (10cm) lengths, and mix all together before building it in. The reason? You get a good balance of moist and dry, and of hard and soft, all in close contact, and the extremes counteract each other. Decay begins from the bruised or cut ends and moves inwards; therefore chopping accelerates decomposition. Build in even layers from 4 to 6 inches (10 to 15cm) thick, add a sprinkle of soil or compost from a previous heap every 6 inches (15cm) or so and give 3 dustings of lime in the process of building. If manure is included, it should be added every 6 inches (15cm), and the lime should not come into direct contact with it.

Use a fork to collect and spread the mixed material. Drive in the prongs occasionally and work the fork backwards and forwards ; this will bring the layers level. If the heap contains loose woody material, a light treading is permissible. This will break down large air pockets formed by crossing stems.

HEAT. Build as quickly as you can and *always* keep a sack over your last layer: it prevents the moist heat escaping from the heap, and is of the utmost importance.

SHELTER. Place a sheet of corrugated iron a few inches above the bin at a slant so as to carry off the rain and allow air to pass over the heap; never use rubber, for it is an insulator.

ACTIVATION. Treat the heap in layers as you build (see page 10).

Forget it for a few weeks. A spring and early summer heap will ripen in 4 to 6 weeks, a late summer and autumn one in 6 to 8 weeks, without turning or any other attention. It is impossible to give an exact date: variations of weather and season, materials, etc., influence the time factor. It may be a little more, or a little less—you must explore the heap by burrowing with a trowel. If it is ripe the compost will break up and will smell sweet ; you will be surprised at the transformation of a green vegetable mass to a warm, rich soil full of humus.

YOUR QUESTIONS ANSWERED

1. *Q. Why should we build quickly?*
   A. Because the intense heat lasts for only a few days. If you add a fresh layer when the heat is high (it reaches 160°F – 71°C) it passes straight on, infects the new addition and maintains the temperature: it is like adding fuel to a fire. If there is a long gap, the heat dies down and the next new layer has to restart it from scratch and valuable time is lost.

2. *Q. It is difficult to get wood. Are there alternatives?*
   A. Yes, wood is cellular and warm, therefore the best, but you can use brick if you leave five half-brick holes each side for ventilation, or use walls of turf or baled straw. Or you can make a successful heap in the open if you follow this pattern.:
   Open heap. Mark a definite square. Build each layer from the outside to the centre, *i.e.*, the first forkloads outline the square. The second forkfuls lie inside and slightly overlap the first: the third and fourth follow the same pattern, and the

final addition goes on the centre and steadies the whole layer. Keep each layer flat and tidy. Continue this pattern layer by layer for 3 ft. (90cm) Keep the sides straight and finish with a domed top. You will then have a firm, compact heap. Cover the sides and top with grass clods, clamp them on (grass down, roots up): they cling to the sides and give splendid protection.

Keep a sack on it while you are building, and add the soil and lime in the normal way. Treat it with Q.R. as you build and forget it until it is ripe.

3. *Q. Can we increase the heat?*
   A. Yes. You can put a weighted board or flat stones on the covering sacks. This not only increases but maintains the heat. The inclusion of wet and bruised nettles will also raise the heat.

4. *Q. How long should we take to build a heap?*
   A. A month is good: two months the outside limit. You can always divide a bin and finish and treat one half before you start the other.

5. *Q. Why do you use lime?*
   A. It sweetens the heap.

6. *Q. Why can't we make the heap in a pit ?*
   A. Because no air would get to it and surface water would drain in and saturate it. The result of either or both would be putrefaction and smell.

7. *Q. What about seeding weeds?*
   A. Put them in the centre away from the sides and top. The heat will soon kill them.

8. *Q. Can one use rampant weeds?*
   A. Yes. The more they ramp the more vitality they have to give to the heap! They all disintegrate and the heat kills them.

9. *Q. We can't get enough material on our holding. What can we do?*
   A. Get it from outside. There are tons of good stuff wasted. Look around and see - bracken and ragwort; wayside grass, banks of nettles, weed-covered dumps, the clearings of ditches and waterways, sawdust, old tea leaves, chip bedding

from stables, the mowings from the local cricket ground or tennis courts, the clearings of the greengrocers and the weekly market. Seaweed (mix it with living greenstuff and it goes quickly), "cavings" from threshing floors and the surplus straw that is now burnt. It may mean co-operation and community effort, but it is worth it many times over. In the allotment it should be easy for the Association to get together, even to have a "Community Compost Heap."

10. *Q. Why does a compost heap not heat during the winter?*
    A. Because in a temperate zone nature is dormant during the winter months. The microbial life in the soil is no longer active; the movement of growth in plants is greatly diminished, except in the case of bulbs. In vegetable matter there is a definite balance between the speed of growth and the speed of decay but in animal droppings the bacteria are always awake and full of energy, which explains why in the winter months a green compost heap is at a standstill whereas a heap of farmyard manure will go on ripening and produce heat; that is why it is used for hotbeds.

11. *Q. Why do you say nothing about wetting the heap?*
    A. If your material is dry by all means wet it before building the heap. Once the heap is finished water might lower the temperature, exclude the oxygen, result in saturation and putrefaction. There are exceptions in the case of a straw heap or a ripe heap that has dried out, but in each case a "drink" of activated manure water is better. By using vegetable matter as fresh as possible juices will be released to keep the heap moist and properly balanced.

12. *Q. If a heap goes wrong, can it be saved?*
    A. Yes. If a heap is a failure, there is invariably a reason, and always a remedy:
    (1) Heaps that are too dry, usually due to:
    (a) Escape of moist heat (failure to cover last layer).
    (b) Using unmixed over-dry material.
    Remedy: Loosen the heap, pour in 1 gallon (4.5 litres) of activated liquid manure.
    (2) Heaps that are slimy and smell, i.e., putrefaction, the result of lack of air from: *(a)* Saturation.
    (b) No outside ventilation. *(c)* Heavy trampling.
    Remedy: Fork into loose piles, let in sun and air, leave for 24

hours, then add some dry soil and treat it again with Q.R. solution.

(3) A late autumn heap unripe in spring due to:

(*a*) Bad weather. (*b*) Being built too late.

Remedy: Open it. Remove what is ripe. Rebuild the rest with fresh spring green. It will be ripe in a month.

Chapter 3

THE ACTIVATOR

I started work on the Herbal Activator in 1935 and called it Q.R. (Quick Return). It has developed through several stages from a floral liquid to its present form, *i.e.,* a fine and beautifully blended herbal powder containing seven ingredients, 100 per cent organic and very easy to use.

To liquefy it: — Mix a teaspoonful in a pint of rainwater, shake well. Let it stand for 4 hours. It will keep about 3 weeks or more: when it smells sour — discard it. For convenience, we talk of "Q.R. Solution" although the powder is not actually soluble in water, the minute particles being in suspension, each separate from the next.

To use: — Apply the solution by sprinkling it on the various layers as the heap is made. For an average heap 3ft. by 3ft. (90cm x 90cm), use about 3 tablespoonfuls to every 4 to 6 in. (10 to 15cm) layer of material. A 6ft. by 6ft. (180cm x 180cm) heap will need four times this quantity. A convenient sprinkler can be made by using an ordinary bottle with a piece cut out of the cork (a V shape wedge across the base will serve).

An alternative method, if the heap is already built, is to make holes with a crowbar or pointed stake to within 6 ins. (15cm) of the bottom of the heap and 12 to 18 ins. (30 to 45cm) apart. Pour 3 ozs. (6 tablespoonfuls) of the solution into each hole, with a circular motion, so that it moistens the sides of the hole. Fill up the holes with friable soil, pressing it down to prevent air pockets. The drier the soil the more easily it trickles in.

IMPORTANT. Always shake the bottle well as you mix it, and before use. A convenient way of mixing the solution is in a pint beer or lemonade bottle. When you shake the bottle you will notice the ring of foam and the way the water is clouded with thousands of

Adding lime to road sweepings before use.

Building the heap, adding material to the outer wall.

Building a heap with garden waste.

The manure tub of cow pats activated with Q.R.

Strong type of timber compost bin.

Miss Maye Bruce tests a new bin for herself.

A useful type of bin with removable sides and top.

Miss Maye Bruce and Geo. Copley examine a newly opened compost heap.

minute particles; these are particles of the seven different ingredients.

As you sprinkle over the layers or pour into the holes, a fine deposit is left wherever the liquid contacts the material, and each individual particle of this deposit is a centre of its own particular energising force, its power of activation. Thus the process goes on from the top to the bottom of the heap. This small dose of 1 teaspoonful in 1 pint (0.5 litre) will convert 40 cu. ft. (1 cubic metre) of vegetable matter into 1 ton (1 tonne) of vegetable compost.* I have an unshakeable faith in the Q.R. Activator: in the last 17 years no heap has been a failure in this garden.

In the beginning I had visualised a time when everyone would make their own activator as part of the routine work of the year, but in practice very few people have done so. To make the present-day finely ground powder is the job for an expert and is beyond the scope of the amateur. ‡

---

* It will also transform an evil-smelling liquid to an odourless plant food. A correspondent, with both authority and a long gardening experience, described how he had arranged for the collection of a barrel of bedroom slops for use as manure. The stench became overwhelming. He soaked some sand in 3 ozs. of the Q.R. activating solution and scattered it over the contents of the barrel. The sand sank, and in sinking released the powder to do its work. In *twenty-four hours* the smell had gone, and in a week he used the liquid in the garden with good results. Other equally dramatic reports have been received.

‡ These methods must not be confused with those connected with Dr. Rudolph Steiner. He first advocated the use of the above-mentioned herbs in agriculture, as publicly stated by the Anthroposophical Society. The activating solution used in the Q.R. methods is entirely different from the preparations carried out by the societies connected with Dr. Steiner's name.

YOUR QUESTIONS ANSWERED

1. *Q. Must the dose be exact?*
   A. No. The method is very elastic. Nature allows margins as long as her basic laws are followed. A little more or a little less makes no difference. The process is not one of an activator working through material contacts. It is an activating force that might perhaps be explained as an electric impulse or radiation. "Radiobiology" is in its infancy and very little research has been made in the vast question of un¬harnessed natural radiation. Man, so far, has harnessed it in the radio, in radar and in radio-therapy. It is a natural force; therefore, in its free unharnessed state, it must be ubiquitous

and universal. I feel certain that, in the future, scientists will find in it the explanation of some of the "Mysteries of Nature" such as the working of the "trace minerals", the absorption of minerals by plants from the atmosphere and the unexplained power of the vitamins — a vast field for research.

This conviction was strengthened when, two years ago, I met Dr. E. Pfeiffer (one of the leaders of thought and knowledge in the agricultural world in America).
I asked him; "Do you, — or do you *not*, — believe that radiation explains the action of trace minerals in the soil?" He answered tersely: "Not only do I believe it — but it *is* so."

2.   *Q. Does not sulphate of ammonia break down vegetable matter with great success ?*
     A. Sulphate of ammonia certainly disintegrates vegetable matter, but it also unbalances organic life. Scientific research has proved that the group of bacteria that break down sulphates generates a gas (sulphuretted hydrogen) which is poison to microfungi, and microfungi are not merely important but essential to the life of many plants. Where sulphate of ammonia is used, mushrooms, once plentiful, die out. Sulphate of ammonia has a bad name amongst practical farmers. One said to me. "I hate it — it tears the guts out of the soil."

Chapter 4

MANURE AND OTHER MATERIALS

MANURE. Manure is not essential to a successful compost heap — it would be a bad lookout if it were.* But manure is, in itself, an activator, because it contains, in addition to immense numbers of bacteria, enzymes and hormones from the animal's body. When ripe it is rich in humus, and no wonder, for it is vegetable in origin, in fact

---

* I tested this point by excluding all animal manure from special heaps for my own flower garden during a period of four years. There was no difference between the results in the two parts of the garden, the flowers and the vegetables, which are well separated by an orchard and buildings. This experience has been corroborated by reports from all over the country, from towns and suburbs, where the manure difficulty is insurmountable.

it is the residue of plants in an advanced state of decomposition: semi-decayed lawn mowings smell exactly like cow dung.

A manure heap should always be treated with Q.R. in the same way as the compost heap. Treat it with the solution at the rate of 1 pint (0.5 litre) to each 6 sq. ft. (2m²) of surface area of manure. In approximately 6 weeks it will ripen to a rich friable humus and look like three-year old manure. You can handle it with a shovel! There are few uses for fresh farmyard manure except to make a hotbed. Natural rotting often takes six months and during this time a big proportion of the plant foods leach away. Activation with Q.R. prevents this, and if only farmers and smallholders used it as a matter of routine, they could use their manure earlier and halve the labour of moving it.

ACTIVATED LIQUID MANURE. Unfortunately, very few of us can get a load of manure, but a good many people can collect a few pailfuls of some sort of animal droppings—cow, horse, poultry, rabbit or goat - in fact, of some domesticated animal.

Here is a way of making a very little cow dung go a very long way. Sink a tub or a box in the soil, fill it to within 3 ins. (7.5cm) of its brim with fresh cow pats collected from fields, roads or gateways. Most kindly farmers will allow that, and many would even give you a pailful from the cowshed. Treat the full tub‡ with 3 ozs. (6 tablespoonfuls) of the Q.R. solution; keep a cover over it to prevent rain flooding it. You can use it 14 days after treatment. Mix a trowelful in a gallon of water; this makes a full strength liquid manure solution. It is a stock solution. Dilute it to tea colour — 1 pint (0.5 litre) to 1 gallon (4.5 litre). That is what we call "activated liquid manure."

USE IT:
(1) To enrich a half ripe compost heap. Pierce the heap with a fork and pour a pailful over it;
(2) to moisten dry straw or any other dry material before adding it to the heap;
(3) as a direct plant food. All plants love it.

Feed fruit trees by piercing the soil with a fork at 5 ft. (150cm)

---

‡ Fill to within 3 inches (7.5cm) of the brim. If you fill it completely, the contents will overflow as the Q.R. solution makes it bubble and increase in volume.

intervals round the outside branches and pouring 1 pint (0.5 litre) into each set of holes.

NOTE. — The manure in the tub does not turn into compost: it loses its rank smell but keeps its fresh appearance.

DRY COW PATS. If you fill and treat with Q.R. solution a similar box of dry cow pats they will go to a velvety black soil very good for pot plants and special work.

POULTRY MANURE. You can add this direct to the heap in thin layers, but I find the best way is to make it into a separate miniature dung heap in the open. Mix in the litter and a little soil. Wet it once a week with activated liquid manure and treat it with the Q.R. solution. It will soon go to a dark farmyard manure. Use that in thin layers in your compost heap.

LAWN MOWINGS are invaluable for their heating power. Mix them in your regular heap with the more fibrous stuff, either in thin layers or before they go on the heap. A thick layer of lawn mowings is a danger. Without fibre they turn into an airless poultice with the slightest pressure. Therefore a surplus should be composted separately. To do this, mix the mass with old dry leaves, or dry hops or sawdust to the proportions of 3 parts grass mowings to 1 part dry fibre; build this into the heap or bin, but do NOT tread down. Treat and cover with a sack. *

FALLEN LEAVES. In the garden fallen leaves can be very useful to mix with kitchen wastes during the autumn months, when fresh material is not forthcoming. At this time of the year a hot heap can only be obtained by using a proportion of animal manure, but the slower decomposition does not diminish the value of the compost. Care should be taken to mix the leaves thoroughly with the kitchen wastes and any other available material — sawdust which has been treated with urine is a useful 'extra' at this period of the year. The leaves should never be added to the heap in layers or they will form an impenetrable mass and prevent the circulation of air. The heap should be treated with Q.R. as it is built.

Alternatively, make a separate stack of the leaves, with a wire netting surround if you like. Add a little, soil and leave them for 6

---

*A box 18 in. by 15 in. by 15 in. (45cm x 30cm x 30cm) was filled with surplus lawn mowings mixed with leaf mould on July 1st. It had been cut, mixed, boxed and treated within 24 hours. It was rich black compost in 14 days.

months. Then turn them out and treat with Q.R. activator. They will go down to a very rich mould, heavier and sweeter even than ordinary leaf mould. Start this heap and keep it going as a rotation. It is good.

YOUR QUESTIONS ANSWERED

1. *Q. What exactly is humus?*
   A. A soil "rich in humus" means a soil full of decayed or decaying vegetable life. In its finest form it is soil made of vegetable life. It is slightly glutinous because of the bodies of countless myriads of the bacteria which break down vegetable matter; the bacteria die in their millions and add their bodies to the richness of the soil. Humus is packed with released life - vital in itself. I remember some years ago seeing a compost heap made from the sparse growth of a bare hillside — a site for a future house. It was treated and in time I went to see the compost and open the first heap. It was sweet, it was soil slightly richer, but almost exactly like the poor soil of the hillside. "What a lot of soil you used to cover it" I remarked—and dug down. It was all the same. The weeds had gone back to the soil whence they came. Now, after some years of composting, that soil is rich and the compost heap full of humus.

   Moral! The more you use on the land, the richer will be the growth, and by so much will the return be richer.

2. *Q. Can one make liquid manure out of vegetable compost? If so, how?*
   A. Yes, and in the same proportions—a trowelful to a gallon as stock solution, diluted further to tea colour. It is exceedingly good.

3. *Q. Does Q.R. improve the manure heap?*
   A. Undoubtedly, and in many ways. (1) Because it makes it friable. (2) It hastens the time of ripening. (3) It prevents leaching of plant foods and so increases both the quality and quantity of crops grown on it. These statements have been proved by practical experience of years, and by actual tests.

4. *Q. How does Q.R. affect the heap?*
   A. Mainly because it stimulates the reproduction of soil micro-organisms.

5. *Q. How can you balance a farm manure heap?*
   A. By adding fresh vegetable matter: weeds, grass, nettles, bracken—anything green and alive. Animal manure is plant refuse plus animal digestive juices, minus plant vitality which the animal has extracted for itself. By adding the vegetable matter to the manure heap you redress the balance and get better results.

6. *Q. Can one make compost on a large scale — such as a nursery garden or on a commercial basis?*
   A. Undoubtedly. Mr. Chase (Jocelyn Chase — Soil Association member and Managing Director of Chase Organics at that time (A.E.D)) makes 2,000 tons (2000 tonnes) a year. He gets raw materials from outside, *i.e.* canal cleanings, sawdust, coffee grounds, farm manure, and all refuse from his gardens. He shreds everything with a mechanical shredder. The heaps are built in long clamps, and turned once with a mechanical muck-shifter. Many nurseries construct their heaps where they will be needed when ripe.

Chapter 5

HOW TO USE THE COMPOST

Work the compost into the top 4 to 6 ins. (10 to 15cm). of the soil; never bury it deep. The soil bacteria live near the surface where they can breathe. For a general dressing use it at the rate of 10 tons (10 tonnes) to the acre (about 5 lb. to a square yard (2.2kg to a square metre)). You will do no harm by giving too much, it will never sour the land. On the other hand the smallest amount will help. If you have not enough to broadcast, give a spadeful to individual plants or rows. The effect of the compost is not confined to material contact; it affects the ground over a wider area. It alters the nature of the soil; breaks down clay, gives light soil substance and sandy soil cohesion. It changes the colour of poor soil to a dark warm brown, turning black after rain. Its action is on the life in the soil; it brings vitality, it creates or recreates a "living soil." That is why all plants enjoy it. They find in it what they need, and can take what they want. No artificial stimulants are forced upon them, therefore they grow to their own perfection of form, colour, health and flavour, and the soil is a delight to touch and a joy to look at. "Good enough to eat" was the judgment of a passer-by. Some plants need special treatment. The greedy ones!

Strawberries like a heavy mulch 3 ins. (7.5cm) deep worked into the soil. They gain in health, productivity and especially in taste. The old real strawberry flavour returns, as it does to

Raspberries, which like the same treatment and respond in the same way.

Lettuces like a heavy dressing and you can grow several crops in succession on the same ground.

Peas and Runner Beans like a dressing mixed with the soil just around the seed stations, and an extra mulch worked into the top soil. In dry weather a drink of the activated liquid manure, followed by a mulch of compost, should do them for the season. In a normal moist year they need no extras.

One successful grower sowed the seed in pure compost and reported an unusually heavy crop.

For small seeds to be sown in pots, boxes and frames, the best proportions are 5 parts loam to 2 parts compost.

Tomatoes in the house

Tomatoes are a compost-conscious crop. I find that the proportion of 5 parts loam to 2 parts compost is good for a start, and for the first potting. Young plants are placed low in their permanent pots and every time their roots appear on the surface fresh soil is added as follows :

1st dressing : Loam 4 parts. Compost 3 parts.
2nd dressing : Loam 3 parts. Compost 4 parts
3rd dressing : Loam 2 parts. Compost 5 parts
4th dressing : Loam 1 part. Compost 6 parts
5th dressing : Compost 7 parts

FLAVOUR AND QUALITY. One of the main points, valuable to growers, is the improved flavour, which is so marked. Housewives learn that compost-grown cabbages do not smell when they are cooked, and compost-grown potatoes do not turn black when they are boiled; that children enjoy the sweet, nutty taste of the perfect Brussel sprout and, above all in these days, compost-grown vegetables have a feeding power, *i.e.* they are satisfying, whereas doped vegetables taste of little or nothing and give neither pleasure nor vitality.

Cloches and Compost

Compost is essential to cloche work. First, because it holds the moisture, and a moisture-holding soil is absolutely necessary for full success. Another equally important reason is that, with glass protection, leaves, stems, flowers and fruit develop abnormally fast, so you must give the roots extra food if you are going to keep the balance of perfect growth.

Pests

There are several theories to account for the phenomena, but the fact remains — pest and disease do not work the havoc in a humus-fed soil that they do elsewhere. Time and again I hear of pests in non-composted gardens — onion mildew, cabbage fly, invasion and devastation by caterpillars, and the compost garden is either completely free or, if attacked, recovers very quickly. Frequently, I hear of plants being destroyed, "and the only ones that were not attacked were some compost-grown seedlings from a friend's garden." The most likely theory is that pests attack the weaklings — nature's way of eliminating the unfit - and, as with humanity, a well-fed race will resist disease, while an under-fed race succumbs. Good feeding implies vitality in the soil and therefore in the plant. So growers have a great responsibility and a greater opportunity in their hands to serve not only the soil, but the people who live on it.

What about the flower garden ? The same principles hold good. Flowers grown with compost are healthy, their colours deepen and glow, their fragrance is fuller and more expansive and they grow as if they enjoy it.

One point must be made. Good husbandry must go hand in hand with good compost.

Chapter 6

FARMERS AND SMALLHOLDERS

The most important of all compost questions is, "How can it best help you, farmers and smallholders?" You obviously cannot have bins all over the farm, and you must save labour. Both difficulties can be met. Make large-scale heaps in the open. Build in sections 8 ft. square (2m²), 5 ft.(150cm) high.

Finish each section, but build them close up to each other in a long clamp. Activate them as you build, so that the first sections will be ripening as the final sections are being built. Build in layers of 6 ins. (15cm), and if you have only one sort of material, divide the layers either with soil (cattle trodden for preference) or manure, or a layer of nettles. If you have mainly straw, a special technique is needed. Wet each layer of straw on the heap with the activated liquid manure. That is the secret of success. If this is done layer by layer, the moisture gets into the straw. Straw with its hollow stem carries oxygen within itself and there is no fear of putrefaction. As you build, the heap should be treated in the usual way with Q.R. solution. Such a heap treated in December should be ripe and rich in humus by May so that it can be moved with a shovel.

A tank of animal urine can be activated by soaking sand in the Q.R. solution and scattering the sand over the contents of the tank. The sinking sand frees the activator and the liquid can be used in 10 days. It is, of course, perfect for wetting straw heaps. Where no tank is available, make your own activated liquid manure as follows :

Fill a water barrow with strong manure solution, *i.e.,* a gallon (4.5 litres) of manure water* to 20 gallons (90 litres) of water — the stock solution. Dilute this stock solution in a second barrow to a strength of about 1 in 16. This is your activated liquid manure and you must water your straw until it is thoroughly soaked, preferably with a can with a fish-tail spreader.

LABOUR. This work can be done when wet weather prevents work on the land, and in slacker moments.

RESULTS. Lighter labour, as soil will become friable. Increased manurial value — 1 ton (1 tonne) of compost is worth 2 tons (2 tonnes) of manure. This was proved on test work at Haughley Research Farm when 6 tons (6 tonnes) per acre of vegetable compost produced as heavy a crop of potatoes as 12 tons (12 tonnes) per acre of farmyard manure and the compost crop was the healthier. The results in the vegetable garden are corroborated by the results on the farm.

---

*Fresh cow manure treated with Q.R. solution in the usual way, as described on page 17.

THE SOIL ASSOCIATION

Before closing this book I must tell you about a movement which is far greater than any individual method of compost making. It was in 1939 that a great meeting of doctors drew attention to the close link between "soil fertility and public health." These views have gained great and growing support, but what is needed now is constructive action, and that is what The Soil Association stands for.

It was started by Lady Eve Balfour and a body of experts. Its aims are:–

To unite all who believe in a Living Soil.
To initiate and promote research
To answer questions and give information.
To present the facts to the public and so build up an informed public opinion.

The question is urgent and it affects everyone, producer and consumer, bread earner and housewife. The fulfilment of the programme depends on the backing of the public. The scale of membership is wide.
(For more information about the Soil Association visit the website: www.soilassociation.org
or contact the membership team on 0117 914 2447 (A.E.D.))

FINALE

The keynote of this book is "vitality" — life in the soil. Life and Light are the two things no man has produced or can produce from a test tube. Life and Light are among the miracles of the Universe. We may use but cannot create them. We can observe them, learn from them, co-operate with them, in all humility, gratitude and joy and with a wonder that grows with knowledge. For Light and Life are part of the Divinity in all that is — "The Divinity within the Flower that is sufficient of Itself."

Also on this subject : "Common Sense Compost Making"
by Maye E. Bruce (Publishers: Faber & Faber) (out of print)

"Quick Return Compost Making – The Essence of the Sustainable Organic Garden" by Andrew E. Davenport
(Publishers: QR Composting Solutions) £12.95
Available on line: www.qrcompostingsolutions.co.uk
or telephone orders on: 01434 672594